The children went for a walk. It was a muddy walk.

"What a muddy path!" said Biff.

"Baa! Baa!"
"What was that?" asked Chip.

"Baa! Baa!"
"What is that?" asked Wilma.

"It's a sheep," said Dad. "Put Floppy on a lead."

"Oh no!" said Chip. "A sheep is
stuck in the mud."

The sheep couldn't get out. The
mud was too deep.

"Help me get it out," said Dad.

Dad went to help the sheep.
He sank into the mud.

Wilma and Chip went to help.

They sank into the mud.

Dad pushed. Wilma and
Chip pulled.

They got the sheep out.
"Baa! Baa!" went the sheep.

Wilma and Chip were muddy.
Dad had lost a boot.

Wilma went to get Dad's boot.

"Help!" said Wilma. "Now I'm stuck!"